THE NATUREN

Shells of North American Shores

East Coast Seashells from Canada to the Florida Keys

Text and Illustrations by

Katherine Orr

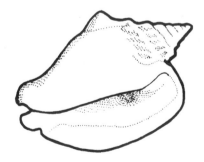

Stemmer
House
Publishers

Gilsum, New Hampshire

MOLLUSKS IN ORDER OF APPEARANCE IN TEXT:

3:1 Stimpson whelk (*Colus stimpsoni*)
3:2 Lyre whelk (*Neptunea lyrata*)
3:3 Waved whelk (*Buccinum undatum*)
3:4 Egg case of waved whelk
3:5 Iceland scallop (*Chlamys islandica*)
3:6 Northern cyclocardia (*Cyclocardia borealis*)
3:7 Wavy astarte (*Astarte undata*)
3:8 Smooth astarte (*Astarte castanea*)
4:1 Clathrate trophon (*Boreotrophon clathratus*)
4:2 Spotted moonsnail (*Euspira triseriata*)
4:3 Amethyst gemclam (*Gemma gemma*)
4:4 Lunate crassinella (*Crassinella lunulata*)
4:5 Northern admete (*Admete couthouyi*)
4:6 Striate cup-and-saucer (*Crucibulum striatum*)
4:7 Alternate bittium (*Bittium alternatum*)
4:8 Ram's horn squid (*Spirula spirula*)
4:9 Atlantic surfclam (*Spisula solidissima*)
5:1 Rough periwinkle (*Littorina saxatilis*)
5:2 Common periwinkle (*Littorina littorea*)
5:3 Yellow periwinkle (*Littorina obtusata*)
5:4 Plant limpet (*Notoacmea testudinalis*)
5:5 Atlantic dogwinkle (*Nucella lapillus*)
5:6 Blue mussel (*Mytilus edulis*)
5:7 Northern red chiton (*Tonicella rubra*)
6:1 Atlantic jackknife (*Ensis directus*)
6:2 Softshell (*Mya arenaria*)
6:3 Northern quahog (*Mercenaria mercenaria*)
6:4 Northern moonsnail (*Euspira heros*)
6:5 Sand collar
6:6 Boreal awningclam (*Solemya borealis*)
6:7 Northern dwarf-tellin (*Tellina agilis*)
7:1 Northern lacuna (*Lacuna vincta*)
7:2 Spiral margarite (*Margarites helicinus*)
7:3 Convex slippersnail (*Crepidula convexa*)
7:4 Bay scallop (*Argopecten irradians*)
7:5 Bowl limpet (*Collisella alveus*)
7:6 Lunar dovesnail (*Mitrella lunata*)
7:7 Greedy dovesnail (*Anachis avara*)
8:1 Ribbed mussel (*Geukensia demissa*)
8:2 False angelwing (*Petricola pholadiformis*)
8:3 Morton eggcockle (*Laevicardium mortoni*)
8:4 Bruised nassa (*Nassarius vibex*)
8:5 Eastern mudsnail (*Ilyanassa obsoleta*)
8:6 Eastern melampus (*Melampus bidentatus*)
8:7 Marsh periwinkle (*Littorina irrorata*)
9:1 Shark eye (*Neverita duplicata*)
9:2 Common jingle (*Anomia simplex*)
9:3 Eastern white slippersnail (*Crepidula plana*)
9:4 Common Atlantic slippersnail (*C. fornicata*)
9:5 Blood ark (*Anadara ovalis*)
9:6 Angulate wentletrap (*Epitonium angulatum*)
9:7 Channeled whelk (*Busycotypus canaliculatus*)
9:8 Knobbed whelk (*Busycon carica*)
9:9 Egg case of knobbed whelk
10:1 Sunrise tellin (*Tellina radiata*)
10:2 Atlantic giant-cockle (*Dinocardium robustum*)
10:3 Turkey wing (*Arca zebra*)
10:4 Atlantic calico scallop (*Argopecten gibbus*)
10:5 Lightning whelk (*Busycon sinistrum*)
10:6 Janthina (*Janthina janthina*)
10:7 Colorful moonsnail (*Natica canrena*)
11:1 Eastern oyster (*Crassostrea virginica*)
11:2 Crested oyster (*Ostreola equestris*)
11:3 Atlantic kittenpaw (*Plicatula gibbosa*)
11:4 Florida rocksnail (*Thais haemastoma floridana*)
11:5 Thick-lip drill (*Eupleura caudata*)
11:6 Atlantic oyster drill (*Urosalpinx cinerea*)
11:7 Impressed odostome (*Boonea impressa*)
12:1 Variable dwarf olive (*Olivella mutica*)
12:2 Calico clam (*Macrocallista maculata*)
12:3 Scotch bonnet (*Phalium granulatum*)
12:4 Atlantic figsnail (*Ficus communis*)
12:5 Rose murex (*Murex rubidus*)
12:6 Southern quahog (*Mercenaria campechiensis*)
13:1 Emerald nerite (*Smaragdia viridis*)
13:2 Flyspeck cerith (*Cerithium muscarum*)
13:3 Tiger lucine (*Codakia orbicularis*)
13:4 Milk conch (*Strombus costatus*)
13:5 Stiff penshell (*Atrina rigida*)
13:6 Pennsylvania lucine (*Linga pensylvanica*)
14:1 Horse conch (*Pleuroploca gigantea*)
14:2 Banded tulip (*Fasciolaria lilium hunteria*)
14:3 True tulip (*Fasciolaria tulipa*)
14:4 Queen conch (*Strombus gigas*)
14:6 Caribbean helmet (*Cassis tuberosa*)
15:1 Broad-ribbed carditid (*Carditamera floridana*)
15:2 West Indian wormsnail (*Vermicularia spirata*)
15:3 Cayenne keyhole limpet (*Diodora cayenensis*)
15:4 Sunray venus (*Macrocallista nimbosa*)
15:5 Rough scallop (*Aequpecten muscosus*)
15:6 Lions-paw scallop (*Nodipecten nodosus*)
15:7 Elegant dosinia (*Dosinia elegans*)
16:1 Florida cone (*Conus floridanus*)
16:2 Variable coquina (*Donax variabilis*)
16:3 Gaudy sanguin (*Asaphis deflorata*)
16:4 King venus (*Chione paphia*)
16:5 Cross-barred venus (*Chione cancellata*)
16:6 Netted olive (*Oliva reticularis*)
16:7 Eastern auger (*Terebra dislocata*)
16:8 Striate bubble (*Bulla striata*)
17:1 Virgin nerite (*Neritina virginea*)
17:2 Flat tree-oyster (*Isognomon alatus*)
17:3 West Indian false cerith (*Batillaria minima*)
17:4 Mangrove periwinkle (*Littorina angulifera*)
17:5 Crown conch (*Melongena corona*)
18:1 Beaded periwinkle (*Tectarius muricatus*)
18:2 Four-tooth nerite (*Nerita versicolor*)
18:3 Scorched mussel (*Brachidontes exustus*)
18:4 Bicolored purse-oyster (*Isognomon bicolor*)
18:5 West Indian green chiton (*Chiton tuberculatus*)
18:6 Deltoid rocksnail (*Thais deltoidea*)
18:7 Bleeding tooth (*Nerita peloronta*)
18:8 Zebra periwinkle (*Littorina ziczac*)
19:1 Flamingo tongue (*Cyphoma gibbosum*)
19:2 Atlantic wing-oyster (*Pteria colymbus*)
19:3 Rough fileclam (*Lima scabra*)
19:4 Atlantic gray cowrie (*Cypraea cinerea*)
19:5 Crown cone (*Conus regius*)
19:6 Frond oyster (*Dendostrea frons*)
20:1 Short coralsnail (*Coralliophila abbreviata*)
20:2 Coffeebean trivia (*Trivia pediculus*)
20:3 Atlantic trumpet triton (*Charonia tritonis variegata*)
20:4 Atlantic thorny-oyster (*Spondylus americanus*)
20:5 Atlantic deer cowrie (*Cypraea cervus*)

2

CONTENTS

INTRODUCTION

As a young child I discovered the joys of gathering and sorting seashells along the New England shore. Of course I soon began wondering why the spectacular shells I saw time after time in colored picturebooks never appeared on *my* beach. Thus began my investigation of shells as living animals. I discovered that different living shells, or "mollusks," live in different regions. I would never find a Pacific spider conch or a glossy deer cowrie washed ashore in Rhode Island. My New England shells may have been drab in comparison, yet because I found them myself and learned about their lives, each became a little treasure.

Most relationships with shells begin when one is attracted by their beauty and diversity. The attraction may remain a simple appreciation for shells as natural art objects, or it may lead, as in my case, to the study of nature and an ever deepening admiration for the interwoven fabric of life on our planet.

This book is not a collection of the world's most beautiful shells. Such a presentation, I think, might reinforce the illusion that shells are really no different from manmade art objects one can buy at a store. Instead I chose to depict the more common shells one is likely to find while walking, wading or snorkelling in the shallows along the eastern seaboard. In this way, the book can also serve as a simple guide for beginning shell collectors and naturalists. By learning to identify shells in the context of where they are found and where their makers live, we are ever reminded that shells are the creations of living animals, each with its own special role and place in nature.

Mollusks, like all living creatures, each have specific environmental conditions under which they live. Those mollusks which live buried in the black mud of marshes are not the same as those one finds clinging to wave-washed rocks or hidden beneath the sands of a clear salt bay. Certain mollusks have adapted to the difficult living conditions of the intertidal zone—that narrow band of shoreline between high and low tides which is alternately covered by sea and exposed to sun and air twice a day. Many more species of mollusk can live only below the low tide line, where a protective blanket of seawater maintains a more constant environment.

If we travel along the eastern coast from Canada to the Florida Keys, we see notable changes in the variety and species of mollusks we encounter. These changes from north to south are caused primarily by water temperature. While many species have a sufficiently broad temperature tolerance to permit them to range along the entire east coast, most cold water inhabitants of the Arctic and Canada extend only as far south as Cape Cod. Temperate water species that are common along the northeastern shores may extend southward as far as Cape Hatteras or the Carolinas, but often they are confined to deep water in the southern part of their range because only at great depth is the water adequately cold. The southeastern shores have a greater variety of mollusks than the northeast since many tropical species are dispersed by the Gulf Stream as far north as the Carolinas. Still other tropical Caribbean species extend only as far north as the Florida Keys. Temperature is, of course, not the only factor affecting mollusk distribution. Pollution, salinity, the abundance of predators and food supply also determine where each species of mollusk lives.

Shoreline explorations along the east coast of the United States will reveal a mixture of living mollusks and their empty shells. Exploration of rocky shores, marshes, sand flats and shallow seabeds will reveal living mollusks. By contrast, few mollusks live along the wave swept seaward beaches because living conditions there are too harsh. Instead, the beachcomber finds the empty shells of mollusks that lived in other areas, perhaps swept in from other shoreline habitats, or tossed up from deep water by storm waves. I have depicted a sampling both of live mollusks in their dwelling places and of their empty shells, cast ashore, to reflect what one may reasonably hope to find.

Shell identification can be a tricky business for the beginner. Unlike birds and wildflowers, members of the same species may vary considerably at maturity in color, shape, texture and even size, depending upon the environmental conditions in which the mollusks lived or the food they ate. Furthermore, some juvenile shells are a different shape or color from their adult forms. The shells in this book are briefly identified as follows:

NAME: Common and scientific names are listed. The scientific name is more important, because although each shell may have several different common names, there is only one correct scientific name for each species of shell.
RANGE: Range represents the northern and southern limits where the shell is known to occur. A shell may be abundant in one part of its range and scarce in another.
SIZE: This represents the average length of an adult shell; actual sizes vary considerably.
COLOR: The colors of typical specimens are described.

In good conscience I must add a cautionary note about collecting. In some places shell collecting has become mass slaughter, such as the commercial trade of shells from the Philippines. Where tourists are thick, even a policy of taking "just one live shell" apiece can wipe out an entire population of mollusks. The policy I was taught as a biologist is never to take a living mollusk unless you can see several others like it nearby; my policy now is to take only empty shells.

The collection of any animal is, in its way, a celebration of nature's wonders. How ironic, then, that collecting live animals harms the very objects of our appreciation. Recognition of this intent—to celebrate, to marvel at shells —may help to guide us away from destruction toward a greater reverence for the living creatures that give them form.   K.O.

4

Acknowledgments

Thanks to Bill Lyons and Donna Turgeon for updating the names of all shells in this book in accordance with those listed in the following publication: *Common and Scientific Names of Aquatic Invertebrates from the United States and Canada: Mollusks*, published by the American Fisheries Society, Bethesda, MD, 1988.

Thanks also to Yosef Kaner for editing and proofreading the text.

1. WHAT ARE SEASHELLS?

Seashells are the outer coverings which surround the bodies of sea-dwelling animals called mollusks. Like the bones of our skeleton, the shell is a part of the living animal; it gives support and shape to the body, and protects the soft tissues within. While still an embryo, the baby mollusk develops a shell. It grows along with the mollusk, and in most cases remains a part of the animal throughout its life. Only after the mollusk's death do we find the empty shells—seashells—scattered like old bones along the shore.

SOME SHELL TERMS

APERTURE The shell opening.

RIGHT-HANDED (dextral) When viewed from the top of the spiral, the shell coils clockwise.

LEFT-HANDED (sinistral) When viewed from the top of the spiral, the shell coils counterclockwise.

INNER LIP The inside border of the aperture.

OUTER LIP The outside border of the aperture.

OPERCULUM The "trap door" that closes off the aperture. The operculum grows attached to the snail's foot and closes the snail inside its shell.

PERIOSTRACUM The papery coating on the outside of a shell. It may be heavy or thin, smooth or "hairy", light tan or dark brown.

SPIRE The spiraling tip of a shell.

WHORL One circle of, or one turn of the spiral.

PROBOSCIS The snail's snout with a mouth at the tip.

FOOT The body part used to move the mollusk around.

MANTLE The fleshy cape of skin that secretes the shell.

SIPHON The tube through which a mollusk pumps seawater.

BYSSAL THREADS, or BYSSUS A clump of sturdy threads, secreted by the foot, that anchors the shell to a rock or other hard surface.

ADDUCTOR MUSCLES The strong muscles used to hold the two halves of a bivalve shell together.

ADDUCTOR SCAR The place where the adductor muscle attaches to the shell.

ANTERIOR END Front end.

POSTERIOR END Back end.

VALVE One of the two shell halves of a bivalve.

HINGE Several teeth that interlock when the valves close.

BEAK or UMBO The top of a bivalve shell just above the hinge.

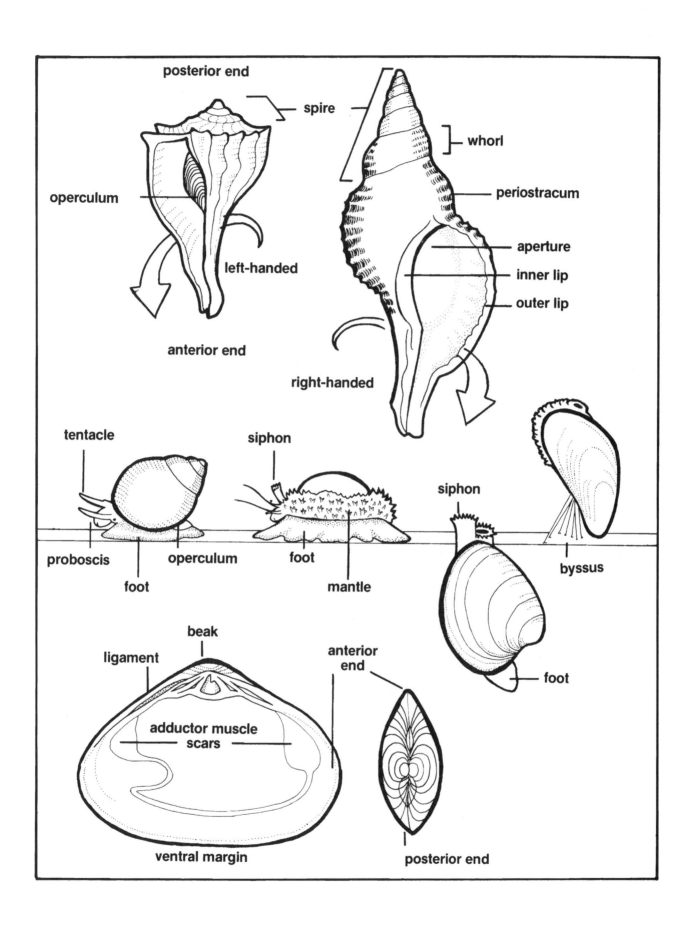

2. MAJOR SHELL GROUPS

Seashells are organized into several groups based on the body of the mollusk and the structure of its shell. On the facing page we see representatives of the most common groups of mollusks.

GASTROPODS constitute the largest group. Each has a single shell which is usually spiral; the animal has two eyes with tentacles, a proboscis (snout) with mouth at the end and a flat foot which glides along the bottom. Gastopods may feed on plants, living flesh, decayed matter or a combination of these.

BIVALVES constitute the second largest group. Each has a two-piece shell joined at one side like a hinged box. The animal must "open the lid" to feed and move around. After the animal dies, the connecting tissue between the two pieces, or valves, often breaks so that we find only one half of the two-part shell washed ashore. Most bivalves feed by gathering small particles from the surrounding water or sediments.

TUSKS each posess a shell which forms a hollow tube around the body. The animal extends its foot and feeding filaments into the surrounding sediments through the large end of the tube. Tusks feed on small organisms in the sediments.

CHITONS (pronounced ki-tans) have flexible shells composed of eight overlapping plates. A large suction foot enables the chiton to clamp its shell tightly onto rocks and other hard substrates for protection. Most species of chiton feed exclusively on plants.

CEPHALOPODS include the squid, octopus, nautilus and cuttlefish. Two members of this group have "shells" which we might find washed ashore. The paper nautilus is not a true shell; it is actually the fragile egg case of the female nautilus. The spirula shell grows inside a tiny deep-sea squid. When the squid dies, its body rots and the gas-filled shell floats to the surface. Most species of cephalopod feed on living animals.

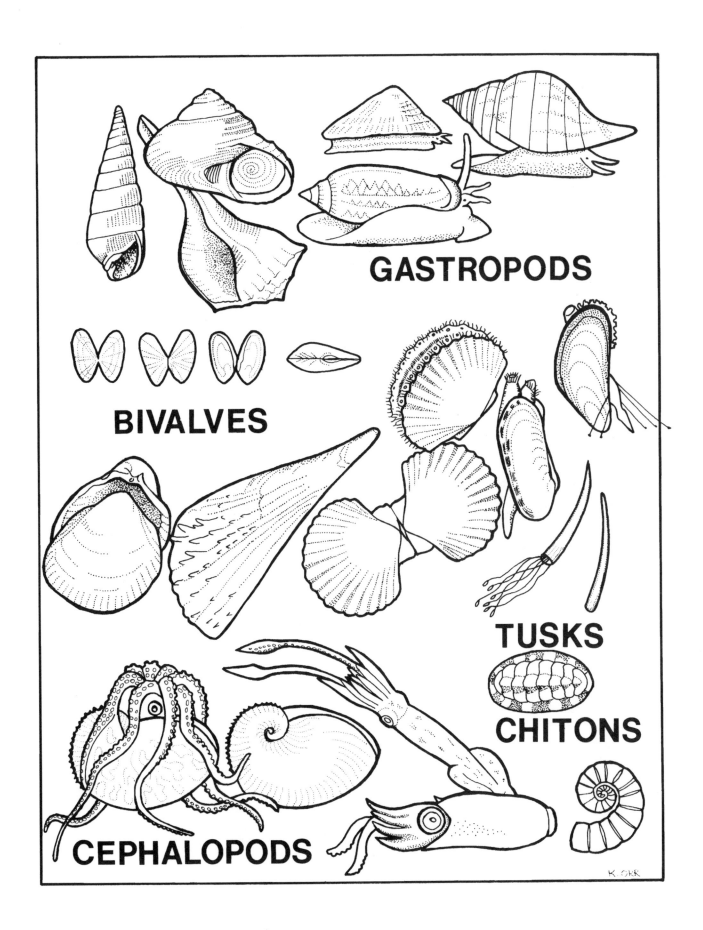

GASTROPODS

BIVALVES

TUSKS

CHITONS

CEPHALOPODS

9

3. COMBING THE NORTHERN BEACHES

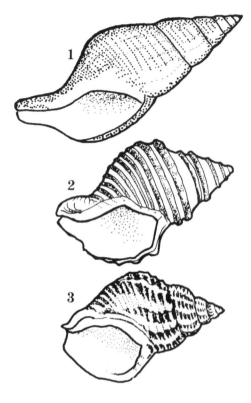

1. Stimpson whelk *(Colus stimpsoni)*
Range: Labrador—North Carolina. Size: 4″
Color: White with dark brown periostracum.
Most commonly washed up on beaches in the northern part of its range where it lives in shallower water.

2. Lyre whelk *(Neptunea lyrata)*
Range: Nova Scotia—Massachusetts. Size: 3″
Color: Grayish/white with reddish-brown spiral cords.
Common on rocky bottoms at 80-90 feet—look for these shells after storms.

3. Waved whelk *(Buccinum undatum)*
Range: Arctic—New Jersey. Size: 3″
Color: Dull white or tan with light brown periostracum.
This predator lives just offshore, where it feeds on clams and dead fish.

4. Egg case of waved whelk
This cluster of small paper-like capsules contains eggs. Some eggs never hatch, serving as food for the baby whelks within the capsules. The baby whelks hatch out of the egg case looking like tiny adults.

4 (Not Illustrated)

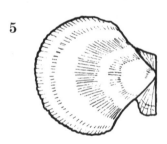

5. Iceland scallop *(Chlamys islandica)*
Range: Arctic—Massachusetts. Size: 3.5″
Color: Usually gray or cream; sometimes yellow, reddish or purplish. These live on coarse sand at 10-300 feet and are fished commercially for food.

6. Northern cyclocardia *(Cyclocardia borealis)*
Range: Labrador—North Carolina. Size: 1.5″
Color: Thick white shell with rough, rusty brown periostracum.
These clams are an important food source for many fish.

7. Wavy astarte *(Astarte undata)*
Range: Labrador—New Jersey. Size: 1″
Color: Exterior strongly ridged and white, covered by a reddish-brown periostracum; interior white.
Very common in mud below the low tide line.

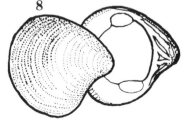

8. Smooth astarte *(Astarte castanea)*
Range: Nova Scotia—New Jersey. Size: 1″
Color: Exterior almost smooth with a glossy brown periostracum; interior white.
Common in mud in fairly shallow water to 100 feet.

4. MORE NORTHERN BEACHES: TINY TREASURES TOSSED ASHORE

1. **Clathrate trophon** *(Boreotrophon clathratus)*
Range: Arctic—Maine. Size: .6"
Color: Chalky-white.
Common on rocky rubble bottoms from 20-200 feet deep.

2. **Spotted moonsnail** *(Euspira triseriata)*
Range: Gulf St. Lawrence—North Carolina. Size: .8"
Color: Yellowish-gray with bands of reddish-brown squares.
This predator feeds on bivalves.

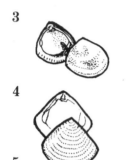

3. **Amethyst gemclam** *(Gemma gemma)*
Range: Nova Scotia—Florida and Texas. Size: .2"
Color: Gray or lavender shading to purple at beaks.
These tiny clams live in fine sand and are an important food source for many predators.

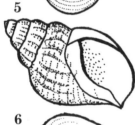

4. **Lunate crassinella** *(Crassinella lunulata)*
Range: Massachusetts—New York. Size: .2"
Color: Yellowish-green; brownish interior.

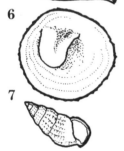

5. **Northern admete** *(Admete couthouyi)*
Range: Arctic—Massachusetts. Size: .5"
Color: Dull white to yellowish-brown.
Look for this shell tossed ashore after storms.

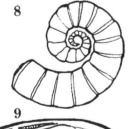

6. **Striate cup-and-saucer** *(Crucibulum striatum)*
Range: Nova Scotia—South Carolina. Size: 1"
Color: Exterior pinkish-white streaked with brown; interior glossy pinkish-brown with white cup.

7. **Alternate bittium** *(Bittium alternatum)*
Range: Canada—Virginia. Size: .3"
Color: Pale reddish-brown, bluish-black or gray.
Feeds on sponges and decayed matter.

8. **Ram's horn squid** *(Spirula spirula)*
Range: World-wide. Size: 1"
Color: White.
This is the internal shell of a tiny squid that lives at great depths. When the animal dies, the shell floats to the surface, often washing ashore.

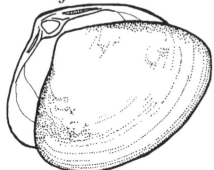

9. **Atlantic surfclam** *(Spisula solidissima)*
Range: Nova Scotia—South Carolina. Size: 5"
Color: Interior white; exterior white with tan periostracum.
In contrast to the tiny shells above, this is the largest northeastern clam.

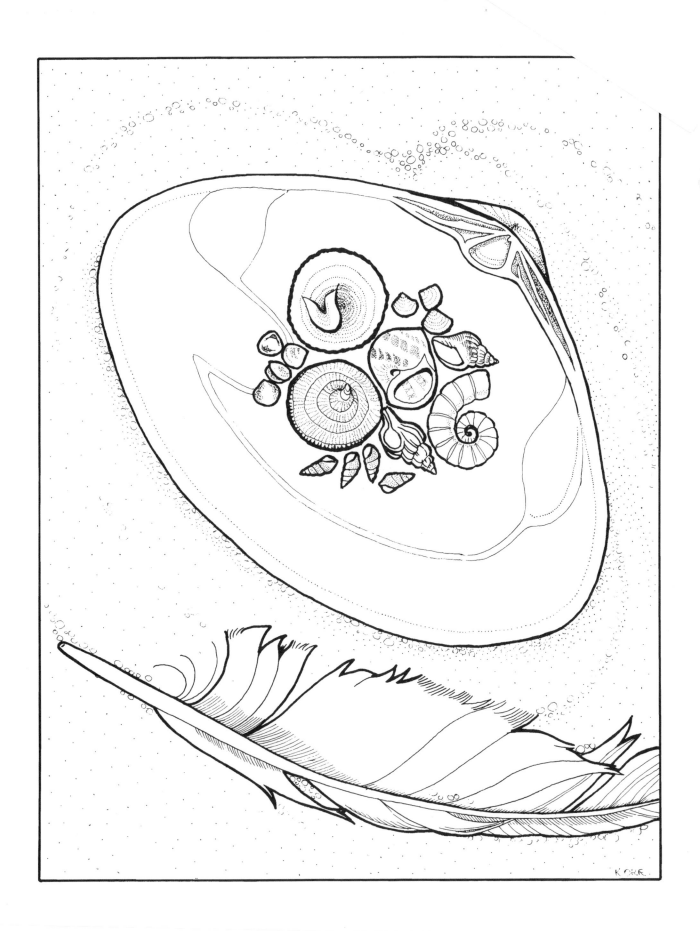

5. NORTHERN ROCKY SHORES AND TIDEPOOLS

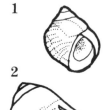

1. Rough periwinkle *(Littorina saxatilis)*
Range: Arctic—New Jersey. Size: .3″
Color: Gray, yellow, greenish, brown or sooty-black. Inside of aperture is brownish-gray or orange.
Look for these periwinkles on rocks above water at low tide.

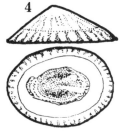

2. Common periwinkle *(Littorina littorea)*
Range: Labrador—Maryland. Size: 1″
Color: Grayish, brownish or blackish with fine spiral bands.
This periwinkle is very common on intertidal rocks and seaweeds near the waterline.

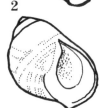

3. Yellow periwinkle *(Littorina obtusata)*
Range: Labrador—New Jersey. Size: .3″
Color: Varies from reddish-brown or orange through yellow to green; sometimes banded.
Look for this periwinkle on rockweed near the waterline.

4. Plant limpet *(Notoacmea testudinalis)*
Range: Arctic—New York. Size: 1″
Color: Interior chocolate-brown surrounded by varied patterns of blue, brown and cream; exterior streaked with brown.
This limpet is commonly found on rocks and shells in tidepools.

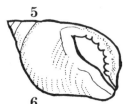

5. Atlantic dogwinkle *(Nucella lapillus)*
Range: Labrador—New York. Size: 1.5″
Color: Varies from white and yellow to grayish and brownish; occasionally banded.
This snail feeds on barnacles and is common on intertidal rocks.

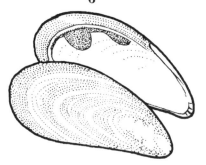

6. Blue mussel *(Mytilus edulis)*
Range: Arctic—South Carolina. Size: 3″
Color: Bluish-black exterior; interior glossy grayish white to dark blue around rim.
Mussels commonly live in large clusters attached to intertidal rocks or pilings by hair-like byssal threads. Mussels are a popular food in many countries.

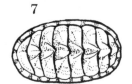

7. Northern red chiton *(Tonicella rubra)*
Range: Arctic—New York. Size: 1″
Color: Light reddish with brown markings; interior rosy.
Look for this chiton under rocks or in crevices.

14

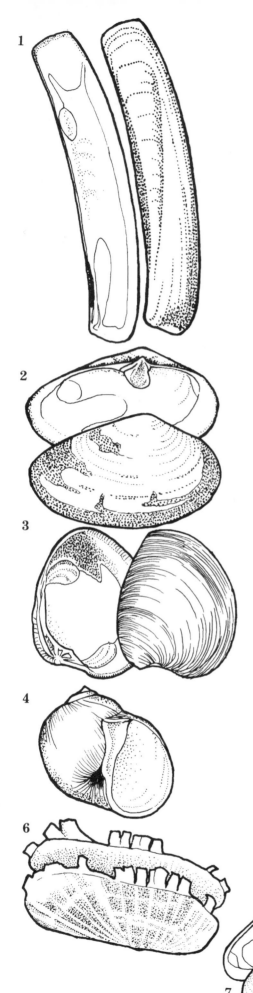

6. NORTHERN MUDFLATS AND SANDBARS

1. Atlantic jackknife *(Ensis directus)*
Range: Canada—South Carolina. Size: 6″
Color: Exterior white with olive green or brown periostracum; interior white.
Commonly lives in colonies in sandy areas near the low-waterline.

2. Softshell *(Mya arenaria)*
Range: Labrador—South Carolina. Size: 3″
Color: White interior; brown periostracum over white exterior.
Lives in sandy mud, intertidally to about 30 feet. Also called "steamer clams" because they are popular when steamed for food.

3. Northern quahog *(Mercenaria mercenaria)*
Range: Canada—Georgia. Size: 3″
Color: Interior white with some deep purple around rim; exterior whitish.
Common in mud and sand from about 2-40 feet depth. Quahogs, or "hard-shell clams", are fished commercially for food.

4. Northern moonsnail *(Euspira heros)*
Range: Canada—North Carolina. Size: 3″
Color: Grayish to brownish with a yellow-brown periostracum.
Common in sandy shallows and deep water where it feeds on buried clams. The living moonsnail has a very large foot and folds of grayish skin which surround the head and shell while it is moving. The fleshy mass helps it plow through the sand as it searches for buried food.

5. Sand collar: the egg case of the northern moonsnail.
As the female snail lays her gelatinous eggs, she surrounds them with this protective ring of sand.

6. Boreal awningclam *(Solemya borealis)*
Range: Nova Scotia—northern Florida. Size: 1″
Color: Glossy brown or greenish-brown periostracum that hangs over the edge of the shell like a fringe.
Builds a U-shaped burrow in shallow sand and mud.

7. Northern dwarf-tellin *(Tellina agilis)*
Range: Canada—Georgia. Size .5″
Color: Irridescent white or rose.
Common in sandy mud.

16

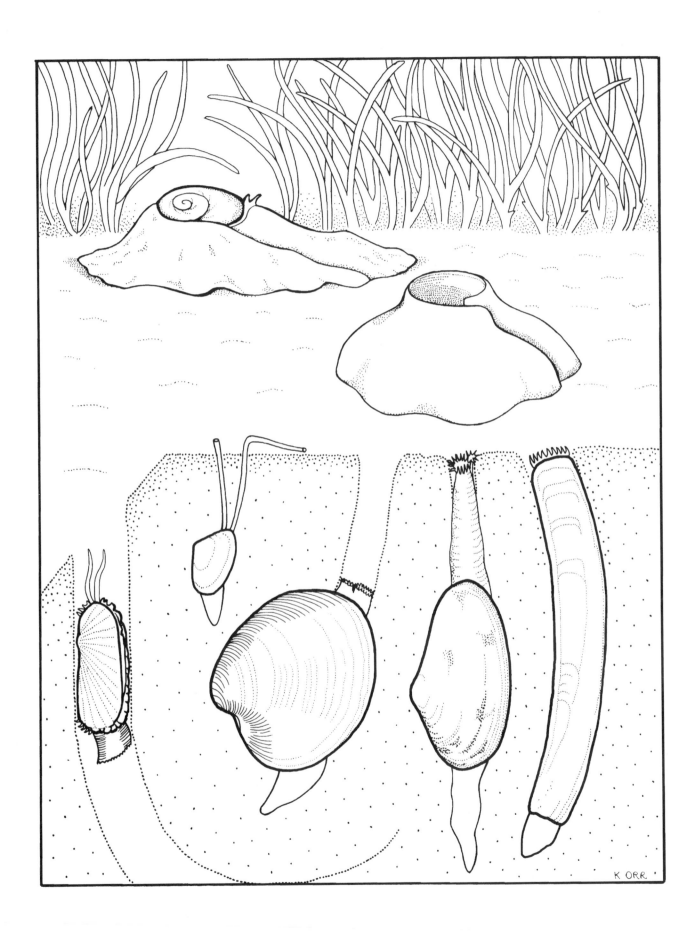

7. NORTHERN EELGRASS MEADOWS

1. Northern lacuna *(Lacuna vincta)*
Range: Arctic—New England. Size: .4"
Color: Shell is thin and translucent; white often with delicate bands of brown or purplish hue.
Common on rocks and weed below 3 feet in depth.

2. Spiral margarite *(Margarites helicinus)*
Range: Arctic—Massachusetts. Size: .3"
Color: Shiny tan or brown with pearly white aperture.

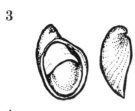

3. Convex slippersnail *(Crepidula convexa)*
Range: Massachusetts—Caribbean; Texas. Size: .3"
Color: Reddish-brown.
Lives on eelgrass. Slippersnails begin life as males and change over to females as they get older.

4. Bay scallop *(Argopecten irradians)*
Range: Massachusetts—New Jersey. Size: 3.5"
Color: Ranges from shades of purplish-brown to bluish-gray; sometimes yellowish-white with dark bands.
Edible. Scallops are able to swim rapidly by snapping the two valves of their shells together. This jet propulsion enables them to escape predators such as the blue crab.

5. Bowl limpet *(Collisella alveus)*
Range: Arctic—New York. Size: .5"
Color: Often checkered with creamy dots.
This oblong form of the plant limpet lives on eelgrass instead of rocks.

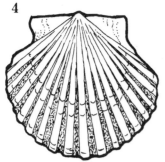

6. Lunar dovesnail *(Mitrella lunata)*
Range: Massachusetts—Caribbean. Size: .2"
Color: Orangy-brown and white.
Common in shallow grass bays.

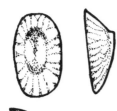

7. Greedy dovesnail *(Anachis avara)*
Range: New Jersey—Florida. Size: .4"
Color: Brownish-yellow.
Look for both dovesnails feeding on soft seaweeds.

8. EASTERN MUDFLATS AND MARSHES

1. Ribbed mussel *(Geukensia demissa)*
Range: Nova Scotia—Florida. Size: 3″
Color: Yellowish-brown exterior; interior glossy bluish-white.
This mussel lives partially embedded in peat marshes.

2. False angelwing *(Petricola pholadiformis)*
Range: Canada—Caribbean; Gulf of Mexico. Size: 2″
Color: Chalky white.
False angelwings bore into dense clay, peat or coral rock and
live hidden from view.

3. Morton eggcockle *(Laevicardium mortoni)*
Range: Massachusetts—Texas. Size: 1″
Color: Glossy shell with bright yellow interior and yellow-
cream exterior with brown markings.
Lives in mud near low tide line. Like other cockles, this clam
is edible.

4. Bruised nassa *(Nassarius vibex)*
Range: Massachusetts—Caribbean. Size: .5″
Color: Gray with white or yellowish around the aperture.
Commonly on muddy sand in shallow water or wet sand.

5. Eastern mudsnail *(Ilyanassa obsoleta)*
Range: Canada—northern Florida. Size: .8″
Color: Dark brown or black, with brownish-purple around
the aperture.
Can be found in great numbers on exposed mud flats at low
tide. This mudsnail feeds on both plant and animal matter,
and is attracted to the smell of dead flesh.

6. Eastern melampus *(Melampus bidentatus)*
Range: Canada—Caribbean; Texas. Size: .6″
Color: Brownish-green to olive; juveniles banded.
This air-breathing snail lives high in the marshes, climbing
grass when the tide rises.

7. Marsh periwinkle *(Littorina irrorata)*
Range: New Jersey—central Florida; Texas. Size: 1″
Color: Cream with reddish bands or dotted bands.
Look for this snail on marsh grasses.

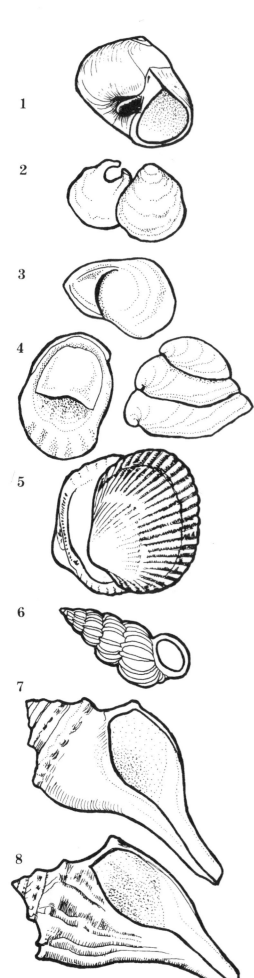

9. COMBING THE MID-ATLANTIC BEACHES

1. Shark eye *(Neverita duplicata)*
Range: Cape Cod—Texas. Size: 3″
Color: Grayish to tan with a purple-brown knob to the left of the aperture.
Common in sandy shallows where it feeds on buried clams.

2. Common jingle *(Anomia simplex)*
Range: Cape Cod—Brazil. Size: 1″
Color: Yellow, orange, white or silvery-black.
Jingles are bivalves that live attached to rocks and other shells. Usually we find only the upper valve.

3. Eastern white slippersnail *(Crepidula plana)*
Range: Nova Scotia—Texas. Size: 1″
Color: White.
These flat shells usually live inside the mouths of empty shells. Look for them in empty moonsnails and whelks.

4. Common Atlantic slippersnail *(Crepidula fornicata)*
Range: Nova Scotia—Texas. Size: 2″
Color: Creamy-tan with brown, pinkish or purplish streaks.
These slippersnails often live stacked on top of one another. Slippersnails begin life as males but change to females as they grow older.

5. Blood ark *(Anadara ovalis)*
Range: Massachusetts—Caribbean; Texas. Size: 2″
Color: White shell with dark brown periostracum.
Blood arks live buried in sandy mud. Unlike most clams, they have red blood.

6. Angulate wentletrap *(Epitonium angulatum)*
Range: New York—Florida. Size: 1″
Color: White.
These wentletraps live on sandy bottoms where they feed on sea anemones.

7. Channeled whelk *(Busycotypus canaliculatus)*
Range: Cape Cod—northern Florida. Size: 7″
Color: Exterior is pale grayish-pink; interior creamy-orange.
Both channeled and knobbed whelks feed on clams and dead flesh. They are fished for food in parts of New England.

8. Knobbed whelk *(Busycon carica)*
Range: Cape Cod—northern Florida. Size: 8″
Color: Cream, often streaked with pale orange and gray; interior creamy-orange to red.

9. Egg case of knobbed whelk
Knobbed and channeled whelks lay a string of papery egg capsules which they attach at one end to a shell or rock. Often these break loose and wash ashore.

23

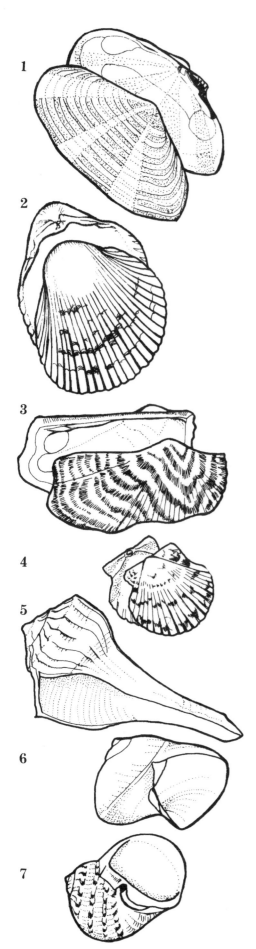

10. MORE GREAT BEACHES OF THE MID-ATLANTIC

1. Sunrise tellin *(Tellina radiata)*
Range: southeastern United States—Caribbean. Size: 3″
Color: Exterior yellow, usually with pink rays; interior yellow.
The sunrise tellin lives buried in sandy bottom.

2. Atlantic giant-cockle *(Dinocardium robustum)*
Range: Virginia—Florida; Texas. Size: 4″
Color: Interior rosy, fading to white around rim; exterior cream with reddish-brown markings.

3. Turkey wing *(Arca zebra)*
Range: North Carolina—Brazil. Size: 3″
Color: White with reddish-brown zebra stripes.
Turkey wings live attached to rocks by byssal threads and are often washed ashore after storms.

4. Atlantic calico scallop *(Argopecten gibbus)*
Range: North Carolina—Brazil. Size: 2.5″
Color: Great variety of colors from purple through yellow; usually with purple and/or orange markings.

5. Lightning whelk *(Busycon sinistrum)*
Range: southeastern United States; in rare instances north to Rhode Island. Size: 6″
Color: Creamy-orange interior; buff exterior with purple streaks.
Notice that this whelk, unlike most other snails, spirals counterclockwise.

6. Janthina *(Janthina janthina)*
Range: tropical oceans of the world. Size: 1″
Color: Violet-purple.
These lovely snails live drifting at sea where they feed on jellyfish; a mass of bubbles, produced by the foot, keeps them afloat.

7. Colorful moonsnail *(Natica canrena)*
Range: North Carolina—Caribbean. Size: 2″
Color: Reddish-tan shell with spiral rows of cream and brown streaks; white around the aperture with brown interior.

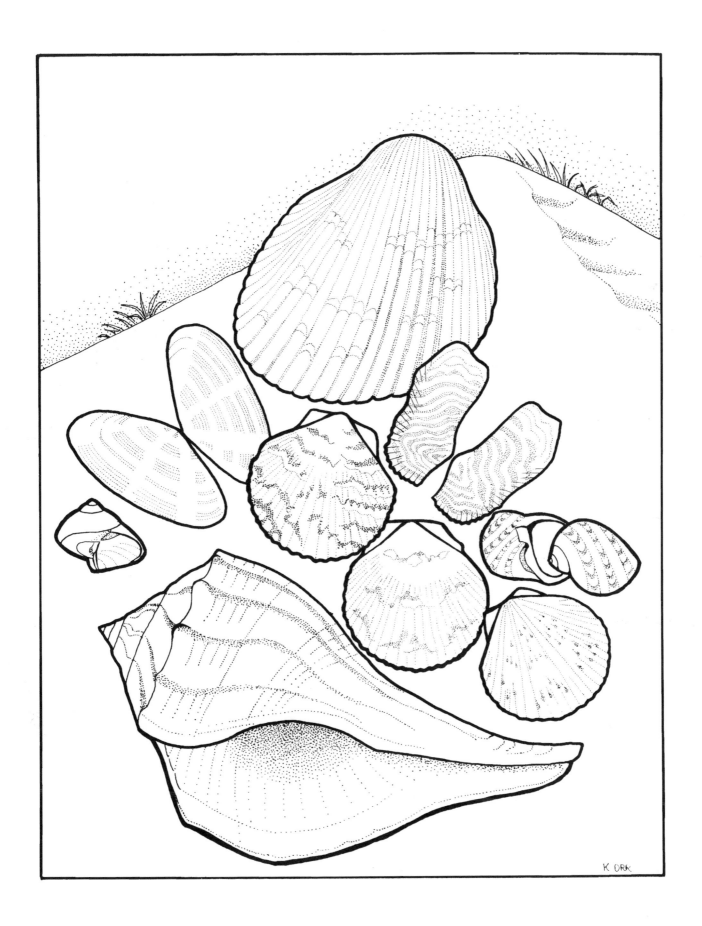

K ORR

25

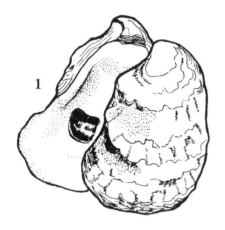

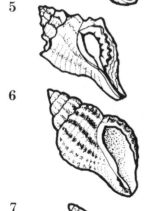

11. MID-ATLANTIC ROCKS AND OYSTER BARS

1. Eastern oyster *(Crassostrea virginica)*
Range: New Brunswick—Gulf of Mexico. Size: 2-6″
Color: Rough grayish exterior; white interior with a purple muscle scar and purple around the edge.
Shell shape and size vary greatly. These edible oysters can be found cemented to rocks in dense colonies along the low tide level. They are fished commercially along the New Jersey shores and Chesapeake Bay.

2. Crested oyster *(Ostreola equestris)*
Range: North Carolina—Caribbean and Gulf of Mexico. Size 2″
Color: Exterior yellowish-gray; interior pearly-green to gray.
Common on subtidal rocks.

3. Atlantic kittenpaw *(Plicatula gibbosa)*
Range: North Carolina—Caribbean. Size: 1″
Color: White interior; exterior white with reddish or gray lines.
Look for these scallops attached to shells and rocks.

4. Florida rocksnail *(Thais haemastoma floridana)*
Range: North Carolina—Brazil. Size: 1.5″
Color: White, gray or brownish-orange.
Common on intertidal muddy rocks and oyster beds.

5. Thick-lip drill *(Eupleura caudata)*
Range: Cape Cod—Florida. Size: 1″
Color: Grayish-white.
Commonly found feeding on oysters.

6. Atlantic oyster drill *(Urosalpinx cinerea)*
Range: Nova Scotia—northeastern Florida. Size: 1″
Color: Gray, orange or purplish; aperture brownish.
This oyster eater is a major problem to the oyster industry.

7. Impressed odostome *(Boonea impressa)*
Range: Massachusetts—Gulf of Mexico. Size: .2″
Color: White.
This snail lives and feeds on bivalves. Look for it clinging to the rim of living oysters and mussels.

12. SOUTHERN SANDFLATS AND SHELTERED BAYS

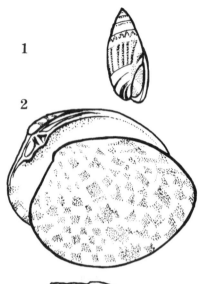

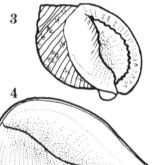

1. Variable dwarf olive *(Olivella mutica)*
North Carolina—Florida. Size: .4"
Color: Glossy cream, sometimes brightly banded.
Lives in shallow sandy mud where it feeds on live and dead meat; foot and mantle partially cover the shell of live olives.

2. Calico clam *(Macrocallista maculata)*
Range: North Carolina—Caribbean. Size: 2.5"
Color: Cream or tan with brown checkered markings; interior white with pale pink tinge.
This edible clam is a popular food in many places.

3. Scotch bonnet *(Phalium granulatum)*
Range: North Carolina—Brazil. Size: 3"
Color: Pale cream with squarish brown spots.
This snail feeds on sand dollars.

4. Atlantic figsnail *(Ficus communis)*
Range: North Carolina—Mexico. Size: 3.5"
Color: Pinkish-cream exterior; interior glossy orange-brown; animal is mottled pinkish-cream and tan.

5. Rose murex *(Murex rubidus)*
Range: South Carolina—Florida. Size: 1.5"
Color: Cream, pink, orange or reddish.
This murex feeds on small bivalves and freshly dead animals.

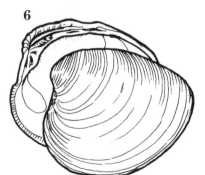

6. Southern quahog *(Mercenaria campechiensis)*
Range: Georgia—Florida. Size: 4"
Color: Exterior white; interior also white, and purple-tinged in rare instances.

K ORR

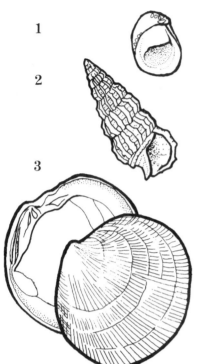

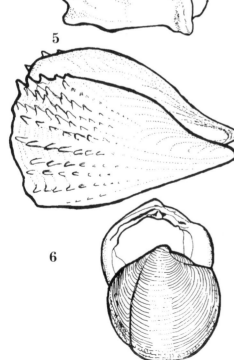

1. Emerald nerite *(Smaragdia viridis)*
Range: Florida—Brazil. Size: .2″
Color: Bright green with white markings.
The snail's body is also bright green, causing it to blend well with the green seagrass blades on which it lives.

2. Flyspeck cerith *(Cerithium muscarum)*
Range: Florida—Caribbean. Size: 1″
Color: White with fine brown bands and speckles.
These snails are commonly found on seagrass blades and other algae of the grass beds (shown here on Merman's shaving brush).

3. Tiger lucine *(Codakia orbicularis)*
Range: Florida—Caribbean. Size: 3″
Color: Exterior white; interior creamy-white or yellowish, with pink border.
This lucine lives buried among seagrass roots.

4. Milk conch *(Strombus costatus)*
Range: Florida—Caribbean. Size: 4″
Color: Exterior white with brown periostracum, and sometimes tan mottlings; interior milk-white; lip turning grayish in older animals.
Like all strombus conchs, these feed on fine seaweeds. The snail's head is greenish-gray.

5. Stiff penshell *(Atrina rigida)*
Range: North Carolina—Caribbean. Size: 8″
Color: Olive-brown.
Penshells live half-buried in sand; byssal threads anchor them to small stones or shells.

6. Pennsylvania lucine *(Linga pensylvanica)*
Range: North Carolina—Caribbean. Size: 1.5″
Color: Exterior white with thin yellow periostracum; interior white.

31

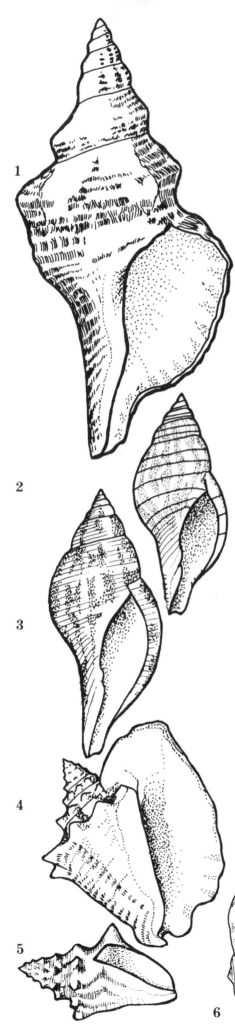

14. MORE SOUTHERN GRASSY SHALLOWS

1. Horse conch *(Pleuroploca gigantea)*
Range: North Carolina—Mexico. Size: 18″
Color: Whitish to salmon with rough brown periostracum; aperture orange.
This is the largest snail to be found in North American seas; it is the state shell of Florida.

2. Banded tulip *(Fasciolaria lilium hunteria)*
Range: North Carolina—Mississippi. Size: 3″
Color: Streaked light purplish-tan with brown spiral bands.
Tulip snails and horse conchs hunt other mollusks for food.

3. True tulip *(Fasciolaria tulipa)*
Range: North Carolina—Caribbean. Size: 4″
Color: Pale with greenish-brown, orange-brown or purplish splotches and faint dark bands; purplish aperture.

4. Queen conch *(Strombus gigas)*
Range: southeastern Florida—Caribbean. Size: 10″
Color: Pinkish with light tan periostracum; aperture glossy shades of pink, yellow, cream or red, with gray in older shells.
Unlike the other snails on this page, conchs are not predators; they graze on plants.

5. Queen conch juveniles do not have the broadly flared lip of the adults.
Color: Young juvenile shells are streaked with dark brown; older juvenile shells pinkish with light tan periostracum. The inner lip is pink; outer lip pink or bright yellow.

6. Caribbean helmet *(Cassis tuberosa)*
Range: North Carolina—Brazil. Size: 6″
Color: Buff, mottled and blotched with shades of brown.
Live helmets are often seen half-buried in sand; they feed on sea urchins and sand dollars.

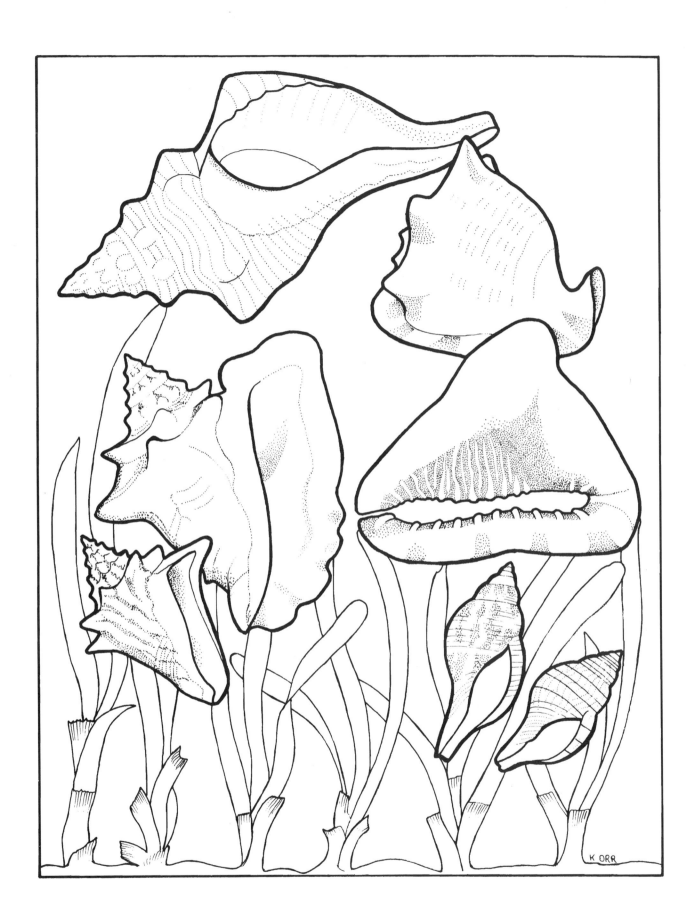

15. COMBING SOUTHERN BEACHES

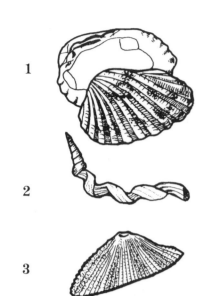

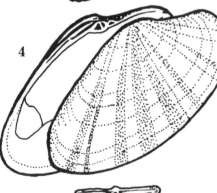

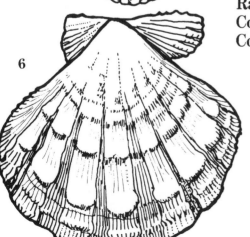

1. Broad-ribbed carditid (*Carditamera floridana*)
Range: Florida—Mexico. Size: 1.2″
Color: Yellowish-white blotched with reddish-brown; interior white.
Common in shallow water.

2. West Indian wormsnail (*Vermicularia spirata*)
Range: southeastern Florida—Caribbean. Size: 4″
Color: Yellowish or reddish-brown, paler toward aperture.
Often found inside sponges in shallow water.

3. Cayenne keyhole limpet (*Diodora cayenensis*)
Range: New Jersey—Brazil. Size: 1.5″
Color: Cream to gray; interior white or gray.
Common on rocks below low tide.

4. Sunray venus (*Macrocallista nimbosa*)
Range: North Carolina—Gulf of Mexico. Size: 5″
Color: Pinkish-tan with purplish markings.
Lives in shallow, sandy mud.

5. Rough scallop (*Aequipecten muscosus*)
Range: North Carolina—Caribbean. Size: 1.5″
Color: Red, orange and in rare instances yellow.

6. Lions-paw scallop (*Nodipecten nodosus*)
Range: southeastern United States—Brazil. Size: 4.5″
Color: Reddish-brown to orange and occasionally yellow.
Lives offshore.

7. Elegant dosinia (*Dosinia elegans*)
Range: southeastern United States—Caribbean. Size: 3″
Color: Glossy white with thin yellowish periostracum.
Common in shallow water.

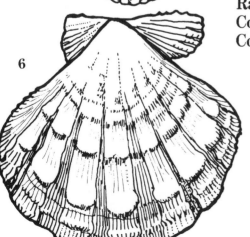

35

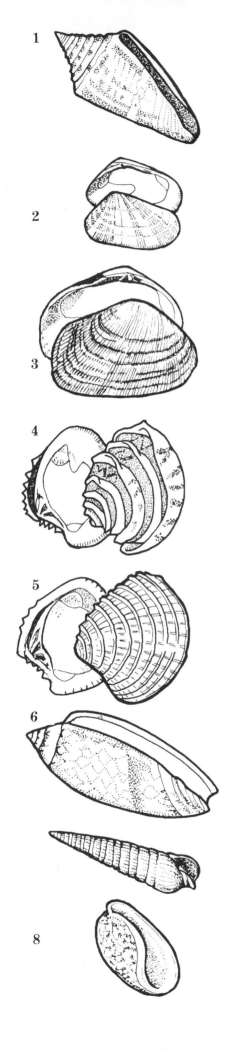

16. MORE SHELLS ON SOUTHERN BEACHES

1. Florida cone *(Conus floridanus)*
Range: North Carolina—Florida. Size: 1″
Color: Usually white with wide patches of orange, and a white band around midsection.
Cones are predators that feed on other animals by paralyzing them with venom.

2. Variable coquina *(Donax variabilis)*
Range: Virginia—Florida and Texas. Size: .7″
Color: Variations include purple, blue, pink, orange, yellow and red; can be plain, marked with rays, bands or a plaid pattern.
Look for these active little bivalves washing in with the waves and burrowing into the beach at the surfline.

3. Gaudy sanguin *(Asaphis deflorata)*
Range: southeastern Florida—Brazil. Size: 2″
Color: Sanguins come in shades of purple, orange, pink, white and yellow.
Look for these on the gravelly edges of beaches. They live buried in gravel between the tide lines.

4. King venus *(Chione paphia)*
Range: southeastern Florida—Caribbean. Size: 1″
Color: White with brown markings.
Venus clams live in sand bottoms where they are eaten in great numbers by crabs and predatory snails.

5. Cross-barred venus *(Chione cancellata)*
Range: South Carolina—Brazil. Size: 1″
Color: Exterior white or gray; interior usually purple.

6. Netted olive *(Oliva reticularis)*
Range: southeastern Florida—Caribbean. Size: 2″
Color: Glossy cream or tan with brown net-like markings.
These predatory animals, like the moonsnails and bubble shells, have a large cape of flesh that partially covers their shell as they crawl, half-buried, through the sand.

7. Eastern auger *(Terebra dislocata)*
Range: Virginia—Caribbean. Size: 1.5″
Color: Pale gray with occasional bands of darker gray and brown.
Found on intertidal sand where they prey upon worms and small clams such as the coquina.

8. Striate bubble *(Bulla striata)*
Range: North Carolina—Caribbean. Size: .8″
Color: Whitish with brown markings.
Live bubble shells live on grassy mudflats.

17. FLORIDA MUDFLATS AND MANGROVES

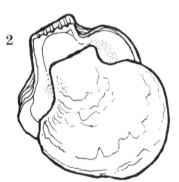

1. Virgin nerite *(Neritina virginea)*
Range: Florida—Texas and Caribbean. Size: .4″
Color: Shell patterns vary widely and colors can include red, green, yellow, orange, black, white, brown and gray.
Virgin nerites live on brackish mudflats.

2. Flat tree-oyster *(Isognomon alatus)*
Range: Florida—Brazil. Size: 3″
Color: Exterior dark brown, purplish-brown or black; interior pearly with brown, purple or black.
These oysters are found growing in large clumps attached by byssal threads to rocks, pilings or mangrove roots, exposed at low tide.

3. West Indian false cerith *(Batillaria minima)*
Range: Florida—Caribbean. Size: .3″
Color: Usually has black and white bands, sometimes brown and white or solid color.
Large colonies of false ceriths can be found scattered across exposed mudflats.

4. Mangrove periwinkle *(Littorina angulifera)*
Range: Florida—Brazil. Size: 1″
Color: Varies from white, bluish-gray, through orange, brown and yellowish.
Look for the living snails on red mangrove prop-roots above the waterline.

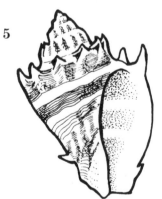

5. Crown conch *(Melongena corona)*
Range: Florida—Alabama, Mexico. Size: 3″
Color: White or yellowish with purplish to chocolate-brown swirls.
Crown conchs commonly live on shady, intertidal mudflats.

18. FLORIDA'S ROCKY SHORES AND TIDEPOOLS

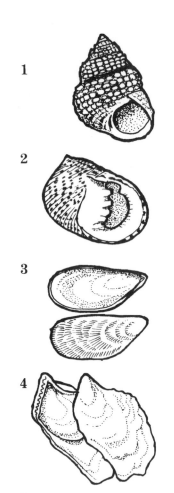

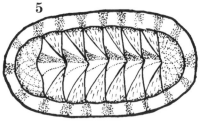

1. Beaded periwinkle *(Tectarius muricatus)*
Range: Florida Keys—Caribbean. Size: .7″
Color: Creamy or gray with orangy aperture.
Commonly found on rocks and dead wood above the high-tide line.

2. Four-tooth nerite *(Nerita versicolor)*
Range: southern Florida—Brazil. Size: .7″
Color: Exterior white with black and pink markings; interior white.
Look for these on exposed rocks at low tide.

3. Scorched mussel *(Brachidontes exustus)*
Range: North Carolina—Caribbean. Size: .7″
Color: Yellowish-brown; dark purplish-brown interior.
Commonly found in clusters on intertidal rocks.

4. Bicolored purse-oyster *(Isognomon bicolor)*
Range: Florida—Texas and Caribbean. Size: 1″
Color: White and purple.
Lives in rock crevices.

5. West Indian green chiton *(Chiton tuberculatus)*
Range: Florida—Caribbean and Texas. Size: 2.5″
Color: Brown or gray marked with shades of black, gray, green or white.
Lives on intertidal rocks, and often looks like a fossil, or part of the rock itself.

6. Deltoid rocksnail *(Thais deltoidea)*
Range: Florida—Caribbean. Size: 1″
Color: Exterior white and brown; inner lip purple or rosy; aperture white.
Common on intertidal rocks.

7. Bleeding tooth *(Nerita peloronta)*
Range: southeastern Florida—Brazil. Size: 1″
Color: Outside yellowish-white with variable patterns of black and reddish-orange; inside has white teeth with a "bloody" orange stain.
Found on high intertidal rocks.

8. Zebra periwinkle *(Littorina ziczac)*
Range: southeastern Florida—Caribbean. Size: .5″
Color: White or bluish-gray with streaks of dark reddish-brown or black.
Found in rock depressions or crevices between low and high tides (intertidal zone).

19. FLORIDA'S CORAL REEFS

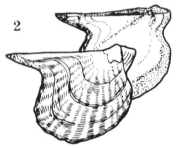

1. Flamingo tongue *(Cyphoma gibbosum)*
Range: Florida—Caribbean. Size: 1″
Color: Creamy-orange with a creamy-white top.
Its shell is usually covered by a mantle of skin with orange, giraffe-like spots.
This snail lives and feeds on soft corals.

2. Atlantic wing-oyster *(Pteria colymbus)*
Range: North Carolina—Brazil. Size: 2.5″
Color: Outside dark brownish-black, often with paler brown streaks; inside pearly.
Look for this oyster attached to the fronds of soft corals.

3. Rough fileclam *(Lima scabra)*
Range: southeastern Florida—Caribbean. Size: 2″
Color: Creamy-white with brown periostracum. The living file-clam has spectacular tentacles of flaming red or orange, some white.
It lives beneath sheltering rock ledges, and can swim rapidly to escape predators by snapping its two valves together.

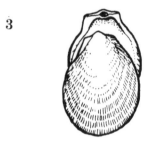

4. Atlantic gray cowrie *(Cypraea cinerea)*
Range: Florida Keys—Brazil. Size: 1″
Color: Face is creamy with dark brown between the teeth; back is pinkish-brown; sides flecked with dark brown.
The live cowrie's shell is usually covered by a "furry" mantle of skin.

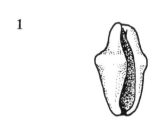

5. Crown cone *(Conus regius)*
Range: southern Florida—Brazil. Size: 1.5″
Color: Usually mottles dark and light brown with white blotches.

6. Frond oyster *(Dendostrea frons)*
Range: Florida—Caribbean. Size: 1.5″
Color: Usually purplish or reddish-brown, interior and exterior.
Frond oysters often live attached to the dead fronds of soft corals.

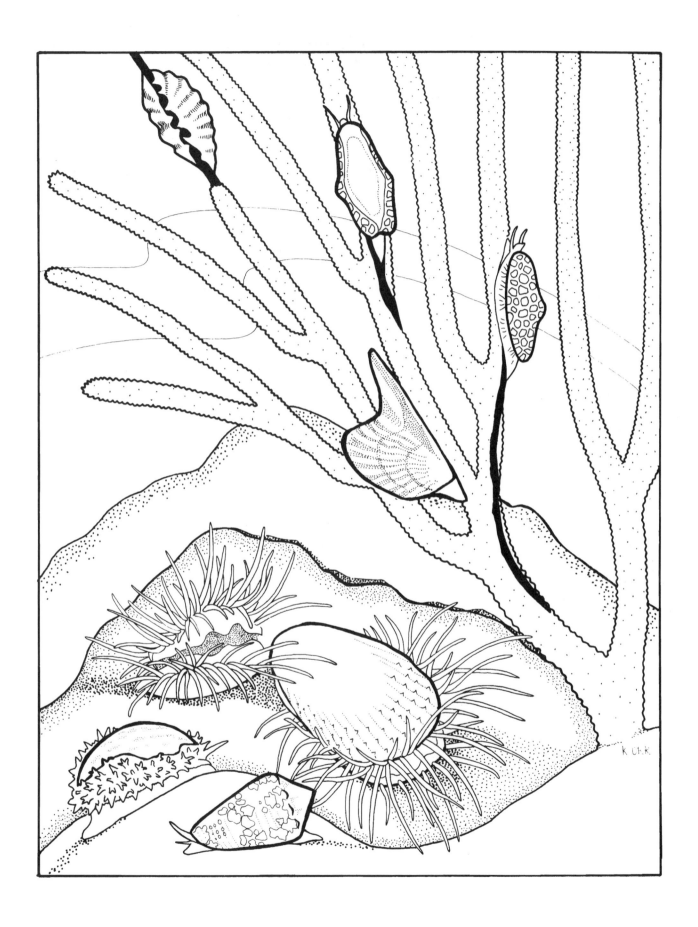

20. MORE CORAL REEFS

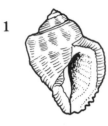

1. Short coralsnail *(Coralliophila abbreviata)*
Range: southeastern Florida—Brazil. Size: 1″
Color: Yellowish-white.
This snail feeds on soft corals and can often be found by searching at the base of soft corals such as sea whips and sea feathers.

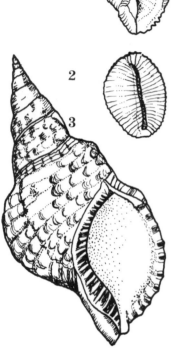

2. Coffeebean trivia *(Trivia pediculus)*
Range: Florida—Caribbean. Size: .5″
Color: Pinkish-tan with 3 pairs of brown splotches.
Trivias live and feed upon small reef animals called tunicates.

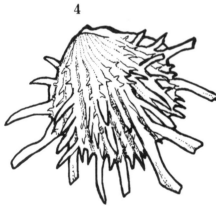

3. Atlantic trumpet triton *(Charonia tritonis variegata)*
Range: southeastern Florida—Caribbean. Size: 10″
Color: Aperture is orange, surrounded by dark brown with white raised ribs; spire marked with shades of white, reddish-brown and black; pink at tip.
The shell of this large, predatory snail was commonly used as a horn, hence the name.

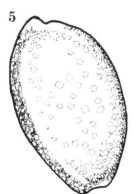

4. Atlantic thorny-oyster *(Spondylus americanus)*
Range: North Carolina—Caribbean. Size: 5″
Color: Exterior varies from white to red, orange, purple and yellow; interior white, rimmed with color.
This oyster lives cemented to reef rock and often becomes so encrusted by other reef plants and animals that it looks like the reef itself.

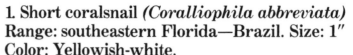

5. Atlantic deer cowrie *(Cypraea cervus)*
Range: southern Florida—Mexico. Size: 4″
Color: Glossy brown with pale spots; sometimes banded with darker brown. Young cowries are banded and lack spots and teeth around the aperture.
Cowrie snails are active at night and shelter by day beneath rocks and ledges.

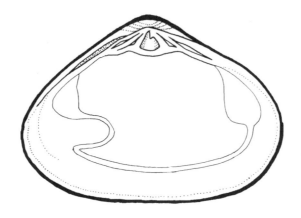

INDEX

Colophon

Designed by Barbara Holdridge
Composed in Helvetica and Century typefaces by
 Brown Composition, Inc., Baltimore, Maryland
Color separation of cover by GraphTec,
 Baltimore, Maryland
Printed on 75-pound Williamsburg Offset and bound
 by St. Mary's Press, Hollywood, Maryland